First published in Great Britain by Heinemann Library
Halley Court, Jordan Hill, Oxford OX2 8EJ
a division of Reed Educational & Professional Publishing Ltd

OXFORD FLORENCE PRAGUE MADRID ATHENS
MELBOURNE AUCKLAND KUALA LUMPUR SINGAPORE TOKYO
IBADAN NAIROBI KAMPALA JOHANNESBURG GABORONE
PORTSMOUTH NH CHICAGO MEXICO CITY SÃO PAULO

First edition © Éditions Mango 1995

This edition © Reed Educational and Professional Publishing Ltd 1997

Designed by Marion de Rouvray and Celia Floyd
Illustrations by Sophie de Seynes
Printed in France

01 00 99 98 97
10 9 8 7 6 5 4 3 2 1
ISBN 0 431 05436 3

British Library Cataloguing in Publication Data

Royer, Alain

    The resurrection. – (Bible stories)
    1. Bible stories, English – Juvenile literature
    I. Title II. Carpentier, Georges
    221.9 ' 505

Acknowledgements
Our thanks to Jan Thompson and Clare Boast for their comments in the preparation of this book.

Every effort has been made to contact copyright holders of any material reproduced in this
book. Any omissions will be rectified in subsequent printings if notice is given to the Publisher.

BIBLE STORIES

The Resurrection

Written by

Alain Royer and Georges Carpentier

Illustrated by

Sophie de Seynes

One spring day, Jesus and his disciples were walking to Jerusalem. The disciples brought a little donkey with them. They put their coats on its back for Jesus to sit on. They went on to the city with Jesus riding the donkey.

When they heard that Jesus was coming, the crowds rushed out to welcome him. Lots of people laid their coats at his feet. Others cut branches from the trees which they waved or placed on the ground in front of him. They cheered loudly, and welcomed him as their hero.

Jesus went straight to the temple. But he got angry when he saw there was a market in God's house. He tipped over all the stalls and chased the stallholders out, saying, 'This temple is my father's house. It is a house of prayer, but you have turned it into a den of thieves!'

Some of Jesus's enemies sneaked off to the chief priests. They told the priests that Jesus had thrown the stallholders out of the temple.

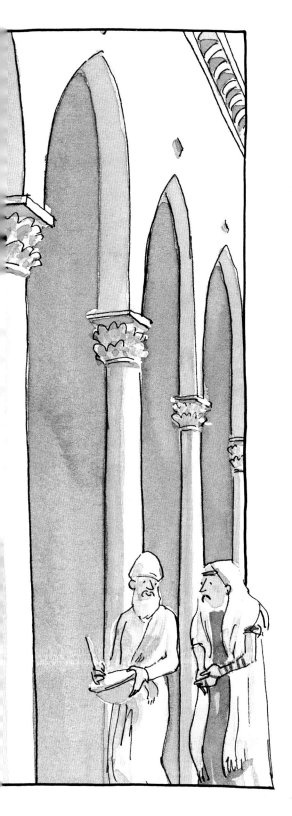

Judas was one of the disciples. A few days later, he went to see the chief priests. He knew they hated Jesus. He planned to hand Jesus over to them. The priests were happy with Judas's plan. They promised to give him thirty pieces of silver when he had handed Jesus over.

On that Thursday, Jesus was with his disciples for the Feast of the Passover. During the meal, he picked up the bread. As he broke it up he said, 'This is my body, which will be broken for you.' Then, taking the wine he said, 'This is the cup of my blood which will be shed for you.'

After the meal, when it was dark, Jesus and his disciples left the city. They went out to the Mount of Olives. Judas had led the guards there. They arrested Jesus. They took him away to the chief priests to be put on trial.

Peter followed a little way behind them, hiding in the crowd. But a maid saw him and said to the guards, 'I have seen that man before. He was with Jesus.' Peter was afraid of being put on trial himself. So he swore three times that he did not know Jesus.

Early that Friday morning, the chief priests took Jesus to Pilate. He was the Roman ruler of the area. Pilate wanted to save Jesus, but the chief priests and the crowd wanted Jesus to be killed.

So Pilate handed Jesus over to be killed. At first the soldiers hurt him and made fun of him. Then they made him carry a cross out of the city, to the top of a hill called Golgotha.

At three o' clock in the afternoon, Jesus died on the cross. That night, two of Jesus' friends took down his body and put it into a new tomb. Then they rolled a big stone in front of the door to the tomb.

Very early on Sunday morning, two women who were followers of Jesus, went to the tomb. They saw that the big stone had been rolled away from the door. They went inside and saw an angel. The angel said to them, 'Jesus is no longer here. He has been raised from the dead and is alive for ever.' The two women ran to tell the disciples what they had seen and heard.